The 21-Day Stress Management Challenge

Learn how to significantly reduce your stress and take better care of yourself in just 21 days

21 Day Challenges

The 21-Day Challenges
Kindle & Paperback

Happiness

Self-love

Self-Confidence

Mindfulness

Stress Management

Minimalism

Productivity

Budgeting

Exercise

Weight Loss

Clean Eating

Introduction

Your sister comes down with a cold and says through red, bleary eyes, "it must be the stress." Your friend at university is reading a book about meditation ...to "reduce stress". Your boss believes the recent deadline has everyone feeling frazzled and suggests a break so everyone can "de-stress".

What is this mysterious thing called "stress", anyway?

Though it has pretty negative connotations, stress is all around us at all times. It's with us when we find the energy to push through a few more hours of study for a big exam. It's there when we're in an emergency situation and need to be completely switched on to resolve things, and quickly. It's there whenever we succeed, when we win, work hard or take a risk.

Since stress is vital for life, I want to start this book with a strange assertion: that we won't be trying to get rid of it at all. "De-stressing" sounds grand, but a person completely free of stress sits (well, *lays*) on the couch, completely unmoved to do anything with life but watch TV and eat.

Stress has many faces and names, and some of those names are *motivation* and *fear* and *excitement*. Sometimes, stress is the only reason we truly understand the worth of the risks we take, or get the chance to stop and heed the red flags all around us. Stress tells us when to stop and rest, tells us, "come on, you can do more than this."

So, we don't want to get rid of stress. Not at all. But we do want to *manage* it.

Stress, like almost everything else in life, is a resource. Too little and you stagnate, too much and you're paralyzed with fear, overwhelmed and unable to make smart decisions. Think of stress as the strings on a beautiful instrument - when they are pulled too tight, they'll simply snap. But if they're too loose, they're useless for making music. No, the trick with all stringed instruments is that they need to be at just the right tension to make just the right pitch.

Think of yourself right now - are you "in tune"? Is your life a good instrument on which to play out the music you need to?

What kind of stress do you have in your life, right now?

Unless you're high on marijuana or have recently won the lottery, then yes, you have stress in your life. Lets get acquainted with it!

Look at the following list and tick all those that apply to you, or have applied to you within the last year:

- money worries - loss of income, debt or stress about employment and making your payments

- getting married - including all the preparation!

- moving to a new home, or emigrating to a completely new country

- chronic illness or injury

- noisy neighbors, uncomfortable living conditions or aggravating housemates

- toxic people; constant fights and altercations with people close to you

- taking care of an elderly or sick family member - even if that family member is furry and has four legs

- traumatic event such as a natural disaster, theft, rape or violence against you or a loved one

- living in an area with overcrowding, crime, pollution or too much noise

- being unhappy in your job, or having too many responsibilities or lack of recognition ...or both

- working long hours

- having poor management or unclear expectation at work

- having no say in the decision-making process and feeling powerless in your organization

- being insecure about your chance for advancement or risk of termination

- having to give speeches in front of colleagues or manage teams
- facing discrimination or harassment at work, especially if your company isn't supportive

- family pressure, disapproval or judgment

- being a parent

- relationship troubles, break ups, long distance arrangements

- feeling chronically broke

- feeling lonely, isolated or misunderstood

- facing discrimination based on your race, gender, age, or sexual orientation

- being bullied

- losing your job or not being able to find work

- death or illness of a loved one

- divorce

- new job, new school, new house, new town

- being incarcerated or dealing with a family member going to jail

- arguments with your spouse, family, friends, co-workers or boss

- job hunting and staying sane during interviews

- important tests

- athletic competitions, races or marathons

- pregnancy, drug abuse, alcoholism, self-harm, insomnia...

- sexual problems and dysfunction

- an unfaithful partner or discovering an infidelity

- a new baby

- the first few months of a new marriage

- debt

- never-ending health issues

- unresolved issues from childhood, past trauma

During this 21-Day Challenge, we'll be seeking first to understand the way we stress and why, and then finding smart, intuitive ways to deal with it. We won't be trying to cultivate the kind of calm of a Zen master with an empty to do list and his taxes already filed. Instead, we'll look at the best ways to live with stress, as you are in your life, right now.

Day 1: finding your stress hotspots

Jenny works at her chaotic hedge fund job for 15 hours a day. She stands over her laptop and wolfs down a sandwich in the 5 minutes it takes her colleague to go to the bathroom, then tries to manage a delicate phone conversation wherein she stands to lose a lot of money and credibility if she doesn't explain herself just right.

During the call, she receives 5 new emails, all of which ping her phone, one of which is URGENT and just at that moment her boss gestures to her to clean up her desk, like he does every day, even though her desk is spotless and he more or less only picks on her this way.

By 5pm, she's trembling, either from too much coffee or not enough, she can't tell any more, and the bumbling cleaning lady who comes in this time every day accidentally knocks over a vase on her table, smashing broken glass and water all over the floor of her office, just at exactly the same moment her phone rings again....

Jenny manages to keep it all together before crumpling in a pile on her couch as she arrives home at 10:30 that night. Suddenly, she notices her dog Buttons has left a suspicious wet spot on the kitchen floor, and seems to be cowering in the doorway. All her pent up rage explodes. "You! I can't take it anymore! You're the problem! I'm getting rid of you first thing in the morning, I can't handle this any longer..."

Amoebas (presumably) have quite a simple take on life. They move towards good things and away from bad, and that's more or less it. Amoebas don't have complicated love-hate relationships with other amoebas or have difficulty locating the source of their unhappiness.

Have you ever "taken out" your stress on the single person most likely to just want to help you? Have you ever gotten home one day with a splitting headache and no idea where it came from? Have you ever had a strong reaction and found yourself saying afterwards, "I don't know what came over me"?

Today's exercise is to start learning *exactly where your stress is coming from*. Poor Jenny could give her dog the boot in the mistaken belief that he's the source of her trouble. The name of the game, as with any self-improvement challenge, is awareness.

Today, track your stress levels as closely as you can. There are a few ways to do this.

- Make a stress "graph" that shows stress levels from one to ten. When you wake up, plot your first stress point and then add a data point each hour of the day. Does your graph spike around lunchtime? When your husband comes home? Late at night when all the bustle stops and you're alone with your thoughts?

- Watch yourself closely throughout the day and try to identify what's stressing you directly. Look for what came immediately before your stressed feelings. Don't just look externally - look internally, too. What thoughts did you have immediately before stressing out? In other words, don't list a source of stress as "my boyfriend" but rather, "the *thought* that my boyfriend is cheating".

- The trick with looking at yourself objectively is that you're most likely to be unaware when you're most stressed. If you're the kind of person who feels like they disappear under a veil of stress, ask hose around you to list a few things they believe to be the source of your stress. In other words, Buttons knows what's going on with Jenny.

- Look back on the last few months and try to think of how many colds and flus you've had, how many angry outbursts or arguments with others. If you have a journal, look back through it and see if you can identify any larger stress patterns. Do you turn into a beast around the time of your period? Are you most stressed around the holiday season? On Sundays when you realize that it's almost Monday again...?

While you watch yourself today, also consider whether you are a chronic or acute stressor, and if you experience your stress more in your body or more on an emotional, mental or psychological level. Perhaps you have a bit of both!

Try to withhold on any judgment right now - you don't have to rush in and force yourself to do a breathing exercise. If you need to yell at your friend, yell. Just take notes and try to understand *why* you do. First comes awareness, then change. Think of yourself the way a scientist would. If your stressful reactions were clues, what truth would they be pointing to?

Day 2: commit

I already know what you're thinking. You look at this section and you think, "ah, here's where she'll say it's important that I dedicate myself to the challenge and blah blah blah, well that's easy, done! Onto the next thing." But wait! Stick around for a second. Most people have a very strange idea of what commitment is.

Commitment is more than saying "I do". Sure, you feel like making the commitment *right now* - why wouldn't you? It's only day 2, you haven't encountered any problems, and the whole thing looks easy and simple enough, right? I ask if you're ready, and you think, duh, of course I am, lets go!

But stay with me for a bit. Here, I don't want you to look far ahead at the end result of this challenge (a less stressed, happier version of yourself) and saying yes to that. Anyone can say yes to that. It's so easy to agree to the good parts that you basically don't have to, it goes without saying. What I'm asking you to do is *commit to the bad parts.*

Here, the commitment I'm talking about is the kind that will carry you through when you feel lazy, or scared, or bored. It's the only thing you'll have to get you through those days when your excuses and rationalizations are strong, and you convince yourself, "it's OK, the rest of the book doesn't really apply to me anyway, I can stop here."

Don't commit to the result, commit to the process. Are you ready to tackle the *real* sources of stress and unhappiness in your life, for the next few weeks? Are you willing to do the difficult, emotional hard work required to make lasting changes to your lifestyle and character? Are you willing to become a little uncomfortable?

This, as you can see, is a different question, and saying "yes" to this is a big deal. It's a promise to yourself. If you know in your heart that you don't intend to follow through with something, all you've done is lie to yourself. All you've done is make it easier to think, "I suck, I'll never finish anything" the next time you are faced with a challenge. You are passing up the opportunity to prove to yourself that you can be more than that.

Commitment is about *just doing it*, no matter what.

It may be true that you hate this book and that it's useless to you, that it really doesn't apply to you and all the rest. But three weeks is not that much time. Commit to it. Whatever happens.

While you muster up the courage to commit, ask yourself the following questions:

- What benefits are you hoping for and why?

- What will your life look like if you keep on going as you always have?

- Why have you resisted changing up till now?

- What are the excuses you're already telling yourself for why you don't have to do the challenge?

Day 3: massages are the best

Today's exercise is to treat yourself to a massage.

Physical touch is not a luxury, it's a basic human need and one of the most simple healing things us human beings can do for each other. An hour massage can completely reset your system, balance your hormones and send waves of relief through your entire being.

Most people have at least some room in their budgets for a professional massage, it's about choices. Or you could ask a friend or partner to give you some relaxation- although nothing beats a professional.

Book your massage for a time when you won't feel rushed to get there, and at a place that's convenient for you to get to. Choose a therapist you like and trust and go with an open, receptive mind. Truly *let go*. Imagine all your muscles and tendons loosening out and releasing all the stress they're carrying. Or, think of nothing at all. Just go into your body and enjoy the sensations of someone caring for you.

If you've opted to enjoy the massage from a friend or partner, make sure they're really willing and that you're not putting extra stress on yourself by judging their technique or worrying that you'll have to return the favor somehow. (although giving a massage in return is very relaxing as well!) There are some truly amazing massage oils on the market, or you can have fun blending your own. Try a base of grapeseed or coconut oil and blend in essential oils of lavender, ylang ylang or neroli. Light a few candles, put on some Enya and let go. Is it cheesy? Sure, a little. But your body and mind will love it. Enjoy, you've deserved it!

Day 4: stop fighting

Tell me if your mom is like this: during Christmas (or any large family gathering), she runs around like a chicken with its head off, stressed half to death about the state of the dessert, or whether your aunt will be arriving soon, or whether the stuffing needs extra pepper or not, or why the dog keeps dirtying the floor, or whether your little cousin is developing a fever, or or or...

Maybe you think to yourself, *there's nothing to stress about.* If she just took a deep breath and a step back, she'd see that everything was fine, everyone was having a good time and that the stress she was feeling was mostly her own doing.

Of course, it's easy to see this in other people, and much more difficult when we ourselves are trapped in a little stress hurricane of our own making. The most obvious thing to do when you're having a hard look at the stress patterns in your life is to see if your stress even needs to be there in the first place.

There is nothing quite so useless in life as fighting against a situation you actually have no power to change. Think about it: the situation remains whatever it is, only you tire yourself out. What's the point?

It's not something that's encouraged much in our culture, but try to *let it go.*

Before you rush off and get stressed and anxious about something, stop and take a deep breath. Ask yourself, what the situation really is (don't interpret and catastrophize, just look clearly at what is objectively happening). Can you change anything in the situation? If so, pour your energy into actions. If not, pour your energy into getting over it.

Can you avoid this situation entirely? Not every problem has a solution, and even if it did, it doesn't mean that *you* have to be the one to solve it. And even if you have to solve it, it doesn't mean you have to do it right now. Stop resisting, stop fighting. Sometimes, the best course of action is no action at all.

Today's exercise is one of gaining control through gaining a more balanced perspective. Pick the three biggest stressors in your life right now. Maybe it's a job you hate or a sick child or an impending divorce or a weird rash on your butt you're too embarrassed to ask for help about.

Ask yourself realistically what measures are open to you to minimize the stress and damage these things can add to your life. *Realistically*. Humans often tend to think we are more responsible and in control than we actually are. In most cases, we are only responsible for a fraction of what goes on in the outside world. Most of the time, our influence extends more or less to our own actions, our own response and our own feelings.

Ask truthfully what actions are possible. What can you change and what can't you?

Jenny can look at her stressful job and think carefully about it. All work is inherently stressful, at least a little, but her job is *particularly* stressful. Though she can take actions to reduce her personal response to the stress of her job, she can't change the nature of the job entirely. Is staying in such a stressful job worth it for her? Are there ways to manage the stress? Is there another job more suited to her needs and goals? Notice how none of these questions involve poor, innocent Buttons.

Day 5: take good care of yourself

Even the most negligent car owner occasionally takes their car for a service. Even technologically ignorant people know to wipe down their keyboards once in a while, and even the most slovenly bachelor knows that his bathroom cabinets need some TLC once in a while.

What is shocking is how resistant people are to giving *their own bodies* the same degree of care and maintenance. When was the last time you went for a medical check up? Had your teeth cleaned? Went to gym and had a good, restful night's sleep?

Think of your body as the vehicle that carries you through life - no other machine is more important. Maintenance might not seem important at the moment, but it *will* seem urgent once you have a problem. Don't get to that point. Care for yourself *before* problems develop.

Today, pick some method of self care that you can keep up for the remainder of the challenge - or think of your own!

- Go to bed an hour earlier, or devote an hour to a sumptuous bath with all the trimmings before you turn in for the evening,

- Start each day with a simple 10 minutes of meditation, journaling or mindfulness practice. One of my favorites is to go to an open window soon after waking up and draw a few deep, slow breaths to start the day.

- Go out into nature for a long walk, or play with your dog. Feed bread to the ducks or do a little bit of gardening to clear your head.

- Give yourself a beauty treatment, a massage (yes, another one!) or make time to put together a new outfit or style your hair differently.

- Sit somewhere quietly with a pot of herbal tea and a good book, or indulge in a movie you've been wanting to see for ages.

- If it's your style, go for a long run.

Day 6: disrupting your automatic stress response

We all know how it goes. It's all well and good to promise yourself you're going to be more mindful and let stressful things go, but then, well, a seriously stressful thing actually happens. You may find yourself getting swept away in the moment before you even realize it. This moment may feel completely out of your control. You may feel like there was nothing you could have done but to respond the way you did - but it's not true!

One of the best skills you can learn in life is to be self aware, not just when it's easy and you're sitting on a cushion somewhere smelling incense. Of course you can be aware and calm under such circumstances! No, the real trick is to maintain that same sense of calm when your three year old has just vomited orange crayon onto your new jacket 4 minutes before you're due to be in a very important meeting.

The trick is to not lose your cool when it would be so, so easy to.

Sometimes, the people around us can see what is happening and step in, telling us that we may be overreacting, or serving as a reminder to take a breath and a step back. But these people aren't always around, and if you're like me, you wouldn't really listen to them anyway even if they were.

Far better is to learn to *interrupt your own stress response*. Now, I'm not asking you to be superhuman and go from raging Hulk lookalike to calm again in a few seconds. That sounds ...difficult to say the least. But much easier and more realistic is the ability to short circuit your stress response *before* it has time to get to Hulk proportions.

The way you do this is by becoming very keenly aware of all the little flutterings and warning signs that precede feeling overwhelmed by emotion. Let's imagine Jenny again, but with an extra dose of self-awareness. Jenny wakes up and immediately recognizes that she's tired from the night before and not her best. She also remembers that her period is due in 3 days and that she might be starting to feel a few grouchy PMS moments. She tells herself to go a bit slower that day. She notices that she's rushing during the day - notices that her heartbeat keeps rising and rising, and that the lunch she scoffed down is giving her heartburn now.

She decides that if she doesn't take a break soon, she'll say or do something she regrets, so she gracefully steps out for a breath of fresh air and to gather her thoughts for a few moments. She notices she feels a bit sharper mentally when she heads back into the office. She also notices that her stress immediately spikes again when her boss walks past her desk, and makes a note of this.

By the time she comes home, she's keenly aware of all the aches in her body, and of how hard it's been to keep her anger in check. By the time she sees Button's telltale puddle on the kitchen floor, all the stress from the day comes out. She realizes: she needs to leave her job. She hugs Buttons and puts her mind on ways to find work that is less stressful and damaging.

Today's task is to keep an eagle eye on everything your body, heart and mind does. Be curious. Catch yourself in stressful moments before they blow up. What is stressing you at the moment? If you're unsure, take a second to remove yourself and gather your thoughts. You'd be amazed at how clarifying a 5 minute walk or a cup of tea can be.

Are you multitasking? Feeling rushed? Are you experiencing negative emotions? Sometimes, anger and stress hide deeper emotions of sadness or feeling powerless. Ask your body how it's doing throughout the day, and listen to the answer you get. Don't ignore tight muscles, sniffles or headaches. Slow down. Are you drinking too much caffeine?

Are you overtired? Eaten something that doesn't agree with you?

Get into the habit of asking yourself as many times in the day as possible: *what do I need to be well right now?*

Day 7: the real irony of "me-time"

Somewhere along the line it became fashionable for women's magazines to recommend carving out "me time" in the busy, modern woman's schedule. Articles about the topic were usually accompanied by a picture of a woman in a business suit and heels with an old school Nokia in one hand and a crying baby balanced on her hip, racing out the door with documents and baby food flying everywhere.

The trouble is, the invective to *just relax* almost became another thing to stress about. Women were encouraged to cough up for hour long facials or retreats that cost and arm and a leg. How many advertisers have you seen that try to convince you to buy their stuff because "you deserve it" and it's a great "treat"?

Ask most stressed women, though, what *really* relaxes them and it's not fancy bubble baths that they're obliged to share on Pinterest or chocolates or "retail therapy". It's not fancy lingerie (being sexy can sometimes feel like just another chore), it's not fancy food (more stress about starting a diet on Monday to make up for it - again) and it's not gifts or presents (after all, what stresses people more than money worries?).

What really relaxes people, more often than not, is being free of all obligations and worries, just for a while. And that also means being free of the obligation of how you're "supposed" to relax. In some circles it's basically heresy to suggest that you don't find yoga relaxing, or that you don't like fancy teas or reading girly romance books. These are all things commonly assumed to be relaxing, the kind of thing you do during your "me-time". But sometimes, you don't want to *do* anything. You don't need to consume or think or meditate or anything at all.

For many people, as unglamorous as it sounds, staying home and tinkering around in the kitchen or blowing a few hours online is more relaxing than putting on whale music and writing in their journals like Oprah says they should.

When was the last time you had real, *genuine* me time? Where you were free to truly relax without any woulds and shoulds and musts? What did you do?

Today's exercise is to reserve some time during the day where you switch of your phone, answer to no one and give yourself a little break of life's expectations. You can do your nails, play video games, paint, try out a new recipe, go for a long walk or literally sit around and do nothing if that is what makes you feel good.

Next, schedule in another date with yourself at some point in the near future. Treat it as you would any other important, unmissable appointment - because it is!

Day 8: reflect

Here are some questions to chew on as you take a pit stop and reflect on your progress up till now.

- What new thing have you learnt about yourself in the last few days?

- In what ways is your stress response a really good idea? How has it helped you all this time?

- If you lived the perfect life with just the perfect amount of stress, what would it look like?

- In what ways is your life already geared up for managing stress?

- In what ways is their room for improvement when it comes to dealing with stress?

- Who do you really look up to when it comes to their way of dealing with life's troubles? How can you learn from them?

- Do you have enough humor in your life?

- What concrete actions so far have you taken to improve your situation?

- What deeper emotions is your stress covering up?

A note about PTSD

In this book, the kind of stress we've been speaking about is every day, "ordinary" human stress that we all experience as the normal price we pay for being alive. Money stress. Relationship stress. That kind of stuff.

If you've experienced something that has been extremely stressful recently, chances are that you may develop posttraumatic stress disorder (PTSD). The trigger could be an assault of any kind, a natural disaster, a death or crime or really anything that at the time had you feeling powerless and completely overwhelmed with stress that you weren't sure you'd survive.

If you notice flashbacks or re-experience the event in any way, if you've found yourself making efforts to avoid certain things to prevent yourself feeling re-traumatized and if you've noticed you're "jumpy", on edge and can't relax, you might be experiencing PTSD. I highly recommend consulting a mental health profession in this case to help you get back on your feet after a horrible experience.

Day 9: cuddle time

If you've ever felt like cuddling that special someone was addictive, well, it kind of is. Cuddling is a great stress reliever since it gives you a big dose of the best legal high out there: oxytocin. Everyone loves to cuddle, and why shouldn't they? Every mammal on this planet knows how good it feels to snuggle up to another mammal, and we love it so much our brains reward us by releasing hormones that make us feel calm, content, safe and happy whenever we do.

Today's exercise is to secure a regular supply of this good stuff. Your next oxytocin dealer can obviously be your partner, and you can get your fix as often as you like with hugs, cuddles and snuggles. Nestle for a second in the warmth of your loved one's neck and you'll discover a pretty potent antidote to the stress and drama of daily life.

But happiness isn't only for partnered people! You can more or less snuggle anyone who lets you, right? :)

Hug your children, your friends, snuggle the dog. If you don't have a pet, carefully consider if you'd like to adopt one (in your considerations you'll have to remember that caring for a pet is around 50% snuggles and 50% cleaning up poo, so be smart about it).

If you're brave enough and live in an open minded sort of place, you may even be able to find "cuddle parties", which are just about as innocent as they sound. You could even try recruiting a cuddle buddy via social media. This is a great way to get out of your comfort zone, get a shot of oxytocin and flex your empathy muscles, plus it makes a great memory for when you're older.

Day 10: sweat!

While we're on the topic of delicious neurotransmitters, let's consider endorphins, the stress reducing feel good hormone that is released during exercise. Exercise improves your mood, relieves tension, improves your sleep, immune system and ability to deal with everyday stress.

It seems that the better able you are to *physically* deal with life's challenges, the easier it is for you to deal with the mental and psychological challenges, too.

Today's exercise is to do something that will make you sweat. You don't necessarily need to go to the gym for this, see if you would enjoy any of the examples I've listed below:

- Call a friend a go for a jog together
- Put on your favorite music and dance!
- Go to the forest for a long walk
- Surprise your partner in the bedroom..
- Follow a hot yoga class
- Have a jump rope competition with your kids

Try to make exercise a regular part of your lifestyle to keep you body healthy and reduce stress on a daily basis. If you're not sure how to motivate yourself, the 21-Day Exercise Challenge can be very helpful. In this challenge I will help you make *and* keep exercise an enjoyable part of your lifestyle.

Day 11: stop complaining and shift your perspective

Most of the time, our reactions to stress are pretty understandable. In fact, most people are quite a bit more resilient than they think they are, and capable of enduring great adversity with good spirits and strength.

Sometimes, just sometimes though, we can be whiny brats about things. It's a paradox - living in the first world with most or all of life's problems comfortably solved for you can actually make it *harder* to deal with little glitches when they appear. In much of the Western world today a serious problem is complaining.

Complaining is one of those insidious problems that will kill you nice and slowly instead of all at once. Complaining is like staring at the great miracle we are all blessed to wake up to every morning, to all the wonders and mysteries built into being alive, to all the opportunities we are given, and saying, "meh, needs more spice".

By merely changing your perspective though, you can remove a whole source of stress that needn't even be there in the first place. Daily niggles, small irritations - these things are almost never worth the effort of the worry we give them, and we would all be so much happier just shrugging them right off.

If you're anything like me, you occasionally get into a mood where you take the fact that the batteries in the remote are flat as proof that God hates you and that you might as well not even bother with life that day and how are you supposed to go on anyway? When life is this unfair?

But it's a good habit to be aware of yourself doing this, and get a little perspective. Because complaining is a form of ingratitude, the best way to start chipping away at a nasty complaining habit is to start paying attention to being grateful.

Today's task is to write in a journal 20 things you are grateful for in your life. Make it a mix of big and little things. What's important is that you have concrete evidence that for the most part, life is actually quite ...nice.

When stress is a warning

Adrenaline is a hormone designed to keep you safe. In the past, life was a bit simpler at least in the fact that the things you'd need protection from more or less came out of the bushes. The solution was to freak out, run away, and that was that.

Today, stressful events are a little harder to pin down, but rest assured that they have the exact same effect on your physical body. Even though there are no tigers in your office and you're at no risk of falling off a dangerous cliff when you get into a fight with someone, your body is *responding* as though it is.

Most of the time, stress is just an outdated kind of response to the new challenges of living in the world we do. Sometimes though, stress is actually a red flag, a warning siren telling you - Freak out! Run way! This is a bad situation!

So, honor that instinct. Use the extra focus to ask yourself honestly - are you in danger? Is your situation one that is conducive to your general happiness or acting against it? Do you need to run away and find something better? Stress could be an inevitable response to difficulties, or it could be a clue that you are where you shouldn't be. Take a moment to decide which one it is. Trust your gut on this - it has evolved over eons and eons and pretty much knows what it's talking about.

Day 12: are you drinking your stress?

A caffeine addiction seems like one of those funny, mostly harmful things, not a true addiction and just something that every working adult is expected to have, to some degree. While it's true that coffee can be enjoyed responsibly, and that when used carefully it can do wonders for boosting mood and concentration, it's also true that it does a lot of damage.

Caffeine is a stimulant. It heightens the body's stress response, which, in small quantities, feels like an energy boost. In reality, the effect is artificial and temporary, and will only wear off. This is fine, except prolonged caffeine use can exhaust your adrenal glands, and throw your hormones off balance. If you are sensitive to caffeine, or already have enough, ahem, *mental* stimulants in your life, caffeine may be just the thing to tip you over the edge. You'd actually be better off seeking a calming, sedative drink like chamomile or valerian tea rather than adding more adrenaline and cortisol to the hormonal fires.

Today, weigh up the pros and cons of having coffee in your life.

- The next cup you enjoy, take careful note of how you feel, mentally and physically. Do you experience craving for more? Shakiness? Dizziness? Does it make you feel better?

- Try to have a caffeine break starting today. If you can't make it three days without coffee, you have proof you've become dependent. Make an effort to get over it and give your body a break. Often trying to quit for a few days and then feeling how much better you feel is all the convincing you need.

- Be aware that there's also caffeine in tea and some soft drinks, even in some medications. If you're going cold turkey, watch out for other caffeine sources.

- Try decaf if you're weaning yourself off, but beware that many are processed with chemicals that are quite bad for you in the long run, so it's best to drink them as a last resort.

Day 13: unplug

You feel lousy about your job, your relationships and your life in general. You're feeling a bit bloated and you wonder if you're starting to get wrinkles. You've had a hard day at the office and it's raining, and when you get home, you log onto Facebook and blam! There it is.

Perfect pictures of a "friend" from High School and her perfect life in perfect Bali or wherever she is on holiday this month. All your other smart, sophisticated friends posting links to articles you're not disciplined enough to read through. You look at your dinner of microwave macaroni and back to the screen where proof of your "friend's" cooking prowess has been broadcast.

Facebook - and all social media - can be hard on the spirit. While the internet offers previously unknown avenues to reach out and connect with all the beautiful people in the world, it can also isolate people. Information overload. Time wasting and distraction. The constant comparison to other people's lives. Stressful social obligations.

Today, try unplugging. Go outside and chat to a person in the flesh. Spend some time alone, or time developing a hobby or skill. Go to the gym. Remind yourself that the picture other people paint of themselves online is about 20% truth and 80% carefully curated fantasy. Learn to shrug things off, keep what's important to you private and try to find other sources of comfort and entertainment.

Day 14: the chapter where I tell you to meditate

For the longest time, I didn't really care about meditating, and in a way, I still don't. But since I found a way to meditate that really fits me and my life, it's a skill and habit I could never do without. Meditation can be a lot of different things, but in every case it means silencing the mind and taking some deliberate time out of your day to become aware of what's going on - both inside you and out. That's all. Quite simple really.

Meditations can be formal or informal, and you can meditate while sitting, walking or even washing your hands. Awareness is, naturally, the kind of thing that just goes well with *living*, whatever it is you happen to be doing.

Today, do the simplest yet maybe most effective meditation I've ever discovered: getting reacquainted with your breath. So much stress comes from simply not breathing enough. Your breath lives in the present moment (and so does the rest of you!) and if you can anchor yourself to it, you'll pull your mind away from stress about the future and worries about the past.

You don't have to do anything special while you breathe. Just take a few moments, a few breaths, to stop, become aware, and listen to your breath. Feel your heartbeat. Notice the air going into and out of your lungs again. Know that, no matter how chaotic life gets, as long as you live you will have this breath, and the ability to just stop and feel it. Beautiful, isn't it?

Day 15: reflect

Today, reflect on the past few days and see if you can come up with an answer on the following questions:

- If you had to write a chapter in this book, what topic would you choose?

- If you were advising a friend on how to reduce their stress, what is the one thing you'd tell them was most important?

- If you could ask any question of a wise man on top of the mountain and knew that he'd tell you the truth, what single question would you ask?

Day 16: it's okay to say "no" and ask for help

Saying no to your own neuroses and complaining and irrational fears is one thing - but it *really* gets interesting when you learn how to say no to other peoples', too. Today, have a look at your life and be honest about how much stress you're carrying for other people.

Don't be a hero about it - are you holding onto and processing stress that doesn't really belong to you?

Today, do two things:

1. Thing one: say no to unnecessary tasks events or ideas that only add stress to your life.

This could range from saying no to your neighbor who keeps taking advantage of your generosity to get free babysitting out of you, to turning down overtime to hang out with family instead. Drop the guilt, drop the friend who you never seem to enjoy spending time with, and drop the sense of obligation for things that only make you unhappy.

2. Thing two: ask for help.

If you're floundering with something and feel like you can't manage on your own, say so. Even just speaking up and expressing yourself is powerful. A lot of people hate feeling vulnerable, but try it today; admit vulnerability, reach out and ask someone else to carry some stress for you, temporarily. In a way, asking for help is an incredibly brave, strong thing to do. After you receive help, try not feel guilty about it. Relax.

Day 17: laugh it off

Have you ever noticed how paramedics and nurses can have the strangest sense of humor? While they deal with occasionally heartbreaking realities in their work, they still make time to be lighthearted, and to not take things too seriously - even life and death doesn't always have to be life and death!

Just like hugging and snuggling, laughing is an effective way to fill your stressed out body with lots of happy chemicals. Enjoy a cheesy pun now and then and play practical jokes on your colleagues. Go to a comedy night or host your own for your cat while you're waiting for the microwave timer to go down. Don't take yourself too seriously :)

There was a time when you - yes you! - were a very silly, very whimsical little child who loved fart jokes and slapstick humor. Humor is resilience. See if you can access that childlike, happy state again and look at the comedy of life today. Try one of the following:

- Rent a comedy to watch. Obvious, I know, but surprisingly effective. Get some kid's cartoons or stand up if that's more your style.

- Tease yourself and others. Here, I don't mean sarcastic or mean spirited, but more playful. So often, the things we think are deadly serious are really not as weighty as we think. Take a breath, see the humor in the situation, take a step back and laugh at how ridiculous life can be sometimes.

- Play. Like a kid. Play tag with your partner to settle who makes dinner that evening or introduce some friendly competition in the office in the form of a weekly game or challenge that everyone joins in on. At my old job, there was a company "mascot" - a cheesy plastic snake - that was hidden all throughout the building for unsuspecting strangers to find, with many laughs to be had by all when it mysteriously appeared in the filing cabinets or behind the cistern in the women's bathroom. It was completely ridiculous, but the ritual bonded us together and made the stress of the job just that little bit easier to deal with.

- Spend time with babies, or animals, or better - baby animals! Kids can have the silliest, most wonderful outlook on life and can really refresh your perspective.

Day 18: relax in nature

There's just something about gazing at a beautiful tree that's been growing for the last 200 years to make all your niggles of last Tuesday disappear into nothingness. Nature is a great perspective giver, a soul-refresher and a good way to unplug the blah blah blah of the overstressed mind. Nature has many lessons if you're curious enough to look. There's the lesson to go slow, to take your time. There's the lesson to be resilient, to make the best of what you have, to see just how full and complicated and connected we all are.

I'm a forest person myself but many people find the ocean is the thing that speaks to their heart, or find they feel peaceful under the moon or in a dry, deserted place. You can buy some flowers to brighten your house, grown your own herbs indoors, borrow a friend's dog or watch a nature program.

Today, try to reconnect to the rest of the world around you - the trees, clouds and birds and feel how it affects your stress levels. They just get on with life in the way that only trees and clouds and birds can.

Day 19: routines

Often times, stress crops up in life as a symptom that we are not being as efficient with our time and resources as we could be. A good solution is to look at your daily schedule and see how much of your stress comes from being late, confusion around appointments or tasks, procrastination or misunderstandings.

If this is a problem for you, your exercise today will be to create some order in the chaos. If you find a lot of your stress comes from rushing in the mornings, try to find ways to plan some things the night before - lay out your clothes, prepare you lunch and leave it by the door, pack your bags and set your alarm for example.

If you're frequently flustered and caught by surprise by things you've forgotten, it may be a good idea to get into the habit of making lists in the morning and prioritizing one or two main items that you'll do first.

If you're frequently late, give yourself a standard 15 minutes more than you think you'll need for every trip or appointment.

If you lie in bed at night stressing about what you didn't do that day, have a journal or next-day to do list to get everything out of your head. Having a calming down ritual every evening before bed often makes a big difference as well.

Lastly if procrastination is an issue for you, consider a few of these ways of getting over this habit, once and for all:

- Force yourself to do a task for just 5 minutes. Often you'll find that once you get going, you're actually fine and can keep on with it way past 5 minutes. Just start.

- If you encounter a chore that will only take a few minutes to do (reply to emails, take out the trash etc.) then do it immediately, instead of letting it hang over you.

- Reward yourself for hitting milestones.

- If you're consistently avoiding a task, take the time to ask yourself if your heart's really in it in the first place. We all have to do life admin at some point, but ever lasting procrastination could be a sign that you're working on something you shouldn't be.

- Delegate! Free yourself up by using an assistant, a colleague's help or simply saying no to tasks that are not that essential.

Reflect on your life and try to come up with a few new habits that will make your day-today life easier and less stressful.

Day 20: you don't have to be perfect

So far in this book we've been concerned about managing stress, reducing it, and generally kicking its butt so we don't have to deal with it anymore. Today, as we get close to the end of our challenge, I'm going to ask you to approach the thing from a different angle, namely, the "so what?" approach.

Being a real, authentic, honest and open person also means being okay with being vulnerable. When we allow ourselves to be vulnerable, we also open ourselves up to deeper intimacy with others, to growth, to new and interesting things. But being vulnerable and out of our comfort zones is... *stressful*.

How can you maintain a fresh sense of awe and vulnerability in the world while not getting stressed and overwhelmed? Well, one way is to reduce stress whenever you see it. The other way is to be okay with stress. To be okay with imperfection, discomfort and confusion.

To say, "well, I haven't got this perfectly figured out yet ...but that's fine. I'm okay with that."

Ta-da! What you've done is something quite magical. You've found a way to be stressed, and yet not stressed at the same time. It costs so much energy to pretend to be someone you're not. To put on a brave face and pretend to have things figured out is not much fun, and it isolates you anyway.

Today, try to be real, authentic, honest and open. Dear to be vulnerable. Be strong enough to admit when you feel weak. Embrace your imperfection - let go of trying to be someone your not and you will notice that your body and mind start to relax and open up.

Day 21: express your emotions and let go..

When you try to shut something up inside a container that it doesn't fit into, you have a problem. Sooner or later, the container can't take it anymore and breaks. Sometimes, stress is actually just pent up emotion that should have been expressed and released way earlier.

Do you have healthy outlets for your emotions - *all* of your emotions? Do you have a space to cry and scream? Do you know how to dance and play when you're overjoyed or how to laugh and draw and talk when you have an idea you're trying to communicate? Do you give yourself the opportunity to feel how you feel, whether it's negative or positive?

Sometimes frustration, anger and stress are just stale old emotions from long ago. When you feel something, feel it. Get it out there. You don't do your body or mind any good by shoving your emotions far away where they can fester and maybe even explode later on.

The opposite of a stressed person is a person who is clear-headed, in control and thriving with life. Stress becomes a problem when it gets in the way of you being effective at your work, or reaching out to connect with others properly. A person who understands their stress and understands how to use it to their advantage enjoys a bit of thrill and challenge, but knows exactly when and how to step back, take a breath and remember what's important.

Many sacred Indian texts end with the invocation, "shanti shanti shanti" which means, very roughly translated, "the peace with surpasseth understanding." Stress is a real practical problem with real, practical solutions. But it also has an emotional and even a spiritual component. Stress is, at bottom, a way of saying that you ultimately don't trust life to do what it does. That you are insecure, untrusting in the outcome of events, watchful in case it all blows up in your face, overwhelmed. There is something deeply spiritual, however, in *letting go*.

In whatever way makes sense for you today, consider letting go and handing off your stress about life in general to a "higher power" or to the world in general. Give it to God, the angels, the fairies in your garden or the memory of your passed grandmother. In fact, let it go without knowing if there is anyone else in the world to give it to at all. Let go and trust that you'll be okay. Draw on the vulnerability you discovered in the previous day's task and expand on it. Tell yourself, "everything is going to be okay" and see if you can really believe it, deep down.

Conclusion

With that, we come to the end of this challenge and the end of this short guide. After three weeks, my hope is that you have stumbled on some useful advice that you'll be able to carry with you for the days that follow this book. Stress requires conscious prevention and intervention. It requires effort to understand, then more effort to manage. Have you managed to learn some of those skills? Have you learnt some things about yourself - good or bad?

Though you totally could get away with it if you wanted, try not to abandon your progress now that you've just gotten started. What happens on day 22 is really up to you, make the best of it and make it a priority to take care of yourself!

Printed in Great Britain
by Amazon